★ **FLICKS** ★

• TOOTH TROUBLES •

• THE BIRTHDAY CAKE •

• RHONDA ROLLS ALONG •

• THE NEW BABY •

AND • A SLEEP-TIME SAGA •

Requests for permission to make copies of any
part of the work should be mailed to:
Permissions, Harcourt Brace Jovanovich, Inc.,
757 Third Avenue, New York, New York 10017

Printed in the United States of America
LIBRARY OF CONGRESS CATALOGING IN PUBLICATION DATA
De Paola, Thomas Anthony.
Flicks.
Summary: Five short "silent movies" include
"Tooth Troubles," "The Birthday Cake," "Rhonda Rolls Along,"
"The New Baby," and "A Sleep-time Saga."
[1. Stories without words. 2. Short stories]
I. Title.
PZ7.D439Fl   [E]   79-87514
ISBN 0-15-228487-7

First edition
B C D E

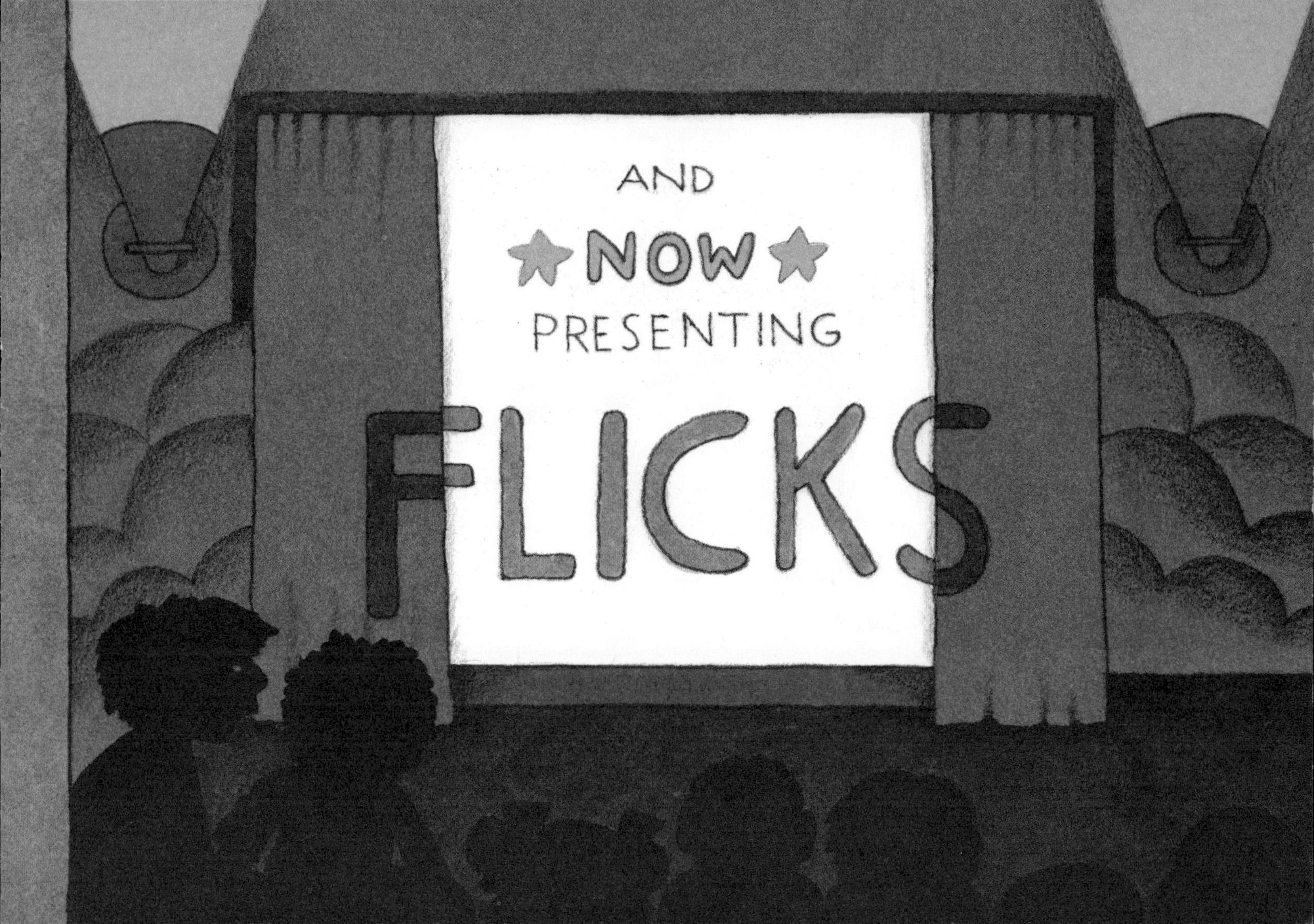
AND
NOW
PRESENTING
FLICKS

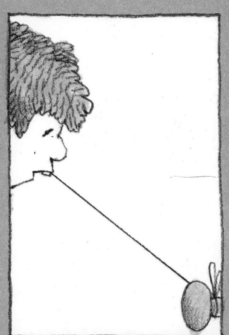

GLADSTONE ELEMENTARY SCHOOL
GLADSTONE, OREGON

THE BIRTHDAY CAKE

RHONDA ROLLS ALONG

and now
a
SLEEP-TIME
Saga